MW00620385

LANDING EAGLE

Inside the Cockpit During the
First Moon Landing

by

Michael Engle

TELEMACHUS PRESS

LANDING EAGLE: Inside the Cockpit During the First Moon Landing

The publisher does not have any control over and does not assume any responsibility for author or third-party websites or their content.

Cover designed by Telemachus Press, LLC

Cover image by Detlev Van Ravenswaay/Science Photo Library
Interior images are from NASA unless otherwise noted.

Published by Telemachus Press, LLC
7652 Sawmill Road
Suite 304
Dublin, Ohio 43016
http://www.telemachuspress.com

Visit the author website:
http://www.MikeEngle.com

ISBN: 978-1-948046-45-9 (eBook)
ISBN: 978-1-948046-63-3 (paperback)

SCIENCE / Space Science

Version 2019.04.10

"Pilots take no special joy in walking:
pilots like flying.
Pilots generally take pride in a good landing,
not in getting out of the vehicle."
~ *Neil Armstrong*

Table of Contents

LANDING EAGLE

Inside the Cockpit During the
First Moon Landing

PREFACE

FIFTY YEARS AGO the Lunar Module Eagle, piloted by Neil Armstrong and Buzz Aldrin, landed on the distant, dusty, cratered plain called Mare Tranquillitatis, the "Sea of Tranquility". Upon landing, Mr. Armstrong christened their landing site as "Tranquility Base", giving it a distinct aeronautical flair. The name is appropriate, for Mr. Armstrong was first and foremost a man who loved airplanes. Or maybe it's more correct to say he loved flying machines in general, and Eagle was the consummate space-flying machine, designed to operate only in the airless void of deep space. Mr. Armstrong, as the first person to pilot this weird-looking contraption all the way down to the surface of the Moon, employed all the aeronautical skills he had learned during a flying career over two decades long. With the able assistance of Col. Aldrin, he skillfully guided Eagle down to a successful landing, in spite of a plethora of problems (some caused by the very automated systems designed to ensure that Eagle could land safely). Together, Armstrong and Aldrin overcame these problems—which included the guidance system overshooting the planned landing site, bad communications with Mission Control, an overloaded computer, inaccurate fuel gauges, and finally a planned landing site that was riddled with rocks and boulders.

In 2001 the NASA Johnson Space Center History Office released the recordings of the audio onboard the Lunar Module Eagle. They were subsequently published in the Apollo 11 Lunar Surface Journal (https://www.hq.nasa.gov/alsj/a11/a11MissionAudio.htm l). These recordings allow us to eavesdrop in on the communications between Armstrong and Aldrin as they flew Eagle down to the surface of the Moon. This book is based on those recordings, and gives a minute-by-minute account of their conversations (in italics) during the twelve and a half minutes from lunar orbit to the landing at Tranquility Base.

PROLOGUE

IN THE SMALL town of Wapakoneta in rural western Ohio, there was once a thriving airport with lush grass runways. It was known as Koneta Airfield. The airport is long gone now, its carefully mown runways replaced by an empty field. It's doubtful that the current owner knows that the first man to walk on the Moon learned to fly there. Over seventy years ago, Port Koneta was home to a busy flight school, where Neil Armstrong and several other young men (and a few young women), sought to become aviators. If you go there on a pleasant summer evening as the sun sets slowly and the sky is taking on the pinkish hue that precedes the coming of the night, it's easy to let your mind drift back to the days when small fabric-covered airplanes carried young fliers aloft from those grassy fields. You might have seen a little yellow airplane with orange trim—an Aeronca Champ—taking off and flying around the field before slowly descending back down to a soft landing, and then doing it over and over and over. The pilot of the Champ is a young man, with a thin frame and cropped blonde hair. He skillfully works the controls of the small plane as he moves into position for another takeoff and landing. This is flight in its most basic form—peering through the windshield, looking for the best spot to land the airplane, carefully judging your altitude and speed and then deftly operating the controls to ensure that you stop your shallow glide, flare out, and touchdown at just the right spot. If you were particularly sensitive and attuned to the motion of the airplane, you could tell if you had the controls coordinated properly by whether your bottom was stationary or sliding across your seat (a trick more colorfully known as "flying by the seat of your pants"). If there's any crosswind, you must also correct for it and make sure you don't allow the wind to blow you sideways, for the Champ can be an unforgiving airplane when landing in a crosswind. The Champ is what pilots call a "stick and rudder" aircraft, one that demands that the pilot master the essentials of flying—the complex interactions between the bank angle of the wings, the direction the nose is pointing, the speed of the airplane through the air, and the sensitivities of the pilot's hands, feet and eyeballs. Even today, in a time when aircraft are electronic and computerized and automated, such skills are highly valued, and to call a pilot a "good stick and rudder pilot" is a high compliment.

A little over two decades later, the young pilot, a seasoned 39-year-old aviator, was at the controls of another flying machine, colored with an odd mix of metallic hues—silver, gold, grey and black. This flying machine was also frail and flimsy; it was the first true spaceship, and would fly only in the quiet, airless void of space, where there are neither clouds, turbulence, storms or lightning, or any of the myriad other threats to machines that fly within the Earth's atmosphere. Today it's orbiting around the Moon, preparing to make a long, shallow approach to a landing on the mysterious surface 50,000 feet below. This flying machine is officially known as a "Lunar Module"—but it's been given a much more glamorous and stately moniker for this particular flight—"Eagle." In many ways, Eagle is similar to that little yellow and orange Champ Neil Armstrong learned to fly back at Port Koneta. It is, in a very real sense, a stick-and-rudder spacecraft, for even though it's computerized in a way that no other machine has ever been, it still depends upon a human pilot to fly it down to a gentle landing. Perhaps Armstrong reflected momentarily on the many days he had spent honing his flying skills, first in the Champ, then in

ever more complex and demanding aircraft as he progressed from student pilot to Naval aviator to NASA test pilot and then to astronaut. What he's about to do will push those skills to the limit and test his mettle as a pilot.

Copyright Dan Patterson, 2019

CHAPTER 1
Designing a Moon Landing

SPACEFLIGHT VISIONARIES HAD been
working on concepts for landing people on the Moon for
decades prior to President Kennedy actually directing
NASA to accomplish this feat. In the mid-fifties, Wernher
von Braun authored a series of *Colliers* magazine articles
about how men would conduct a Moon landing. In his
articles, von Braun told of a fleet of large, airplane-like
rockets embarking from the Earth and flying directly to a
landing on the Moon. The rockets were beautiful machines, pointing to a future where space travel would be
commonplace and elegant, much like the new jet-age airline fleet Pan Am, American, British Overseas Airways
Corporation and others were just then introducing to the
world. Unfortunately, there's a brutal law of physics—
expressed mathematically in something called the rocket
equation—that requires very large (and heavy) booster

rockets to launch such a spacecraft. And with only eight years to accomplish President Kennedy's goal, NASA didn't have the time to develop such a rocket (even though one—called Nova, a giant twelve million pound behemoth—was on NASA's drawing boards at the time). So Wernher von Braun and his team started working on another concept for a Moon landing mission, which could use the Saturn series of rocket boosters already being assembled. This concept involved launching large pieces of the lunar spacecraft on separate boosters to Earth orbit where teams of spacewalking astronauts would assemble the pieces and then fly the spacecraft to the Moon, a scheme called "Earth Orbit Rendezvous." But there was one big problem with Earth Orbit Rendezvous—NASA had no experience with bringing spacecraft together in orbit (a technique elegantly expressed as "rendezvous") or with spacewalking astronauts assembling components in orbit. In May of 1961, when Kennedy formally committed NASA to "landing a man on the Moon and returning him safely to the Earth" before 1970, NASA had a grand total of 15 minutes of spaceflight experience with one astronaut! And that wasn't even an orbital flight, but a simple 100 mile high ballistic lob of the small Mercury spacecraft with astronaut Alan Shepherd aboard. With so little real experience in space, complex activities like spacecraft docking together in orbit and astronauts walking in space—especially on the scale required for Earth Orbit Rendezvous—seemed formidable and out of reach in the near future. And President Kennedy had given NASA less than nine years to get to the Moon. NASA management was nearly in a state of panic.

Fortunately, a few engineers had been kicking around another method for getting to the Moon—something called Lunar Orbit Rendezvous (LOR), which would prove to be the answer to NASA's problems. The concept of Lunar Orbit Rendezvous was originally conceived in 1916 by Yuri Kondratyuk, a self-taught Russian astronautical genius, who had been drafted into the Russian army and somehow found time to indulge his interest in spaceflight while fighting the Germans and Turks in the Middle Eastern Theatre during World War I. Lunar Orbit Rendezvous required two spacecraft, one an orbiting mother ship, which contained the primary propulsion system for entering and leaving lunar orbit, and a second, smaller spacecraft for landing on the Moon. The beauty of Lunar Orbit Rendezvous was that it enabled travel to, and a landing on, the Moon without relying on a huge rocket. It could be done using the existing Saturn-series, including the planned Saturn V, a 363-foot-tall, seven-and-a-half million pound rocket already in development.

Although Lunar Orbit Rendezvous offered the only real hope for NASA to get to the Moon before the end of the decade, it was not well received by NASA management, which was deeply committed to Earth Orbit Rendezvous. In frustration a NASA engineer named John Houbolt risked his reputation—and his career—by going over his management's collective head. He wrote a letter to NASA's associate administrator, Robert Seamans. In the letter he called himself "a voice crying in the wilderness," preaching the truth that Lunar Orbit Rendezvous was the only way to achieve a Moon landing by Kennedy's deadline. Perhaps Houbolt's melodramatic words, so atypical of a NASA engineer, convinced Seamans because he allowed Houbolt to present his case to upper management. After Houbolt's presentation, even the formidable Wernher von Braun, the main proponent of Earth Orbit Rendezvous, was convinced that Lunar Orbit Rendezvous was indeed the right approach. With that decision, the design and construction of NASA's lunar spacecraft began.

The spacecraft that the Saturn V planned to launch toward the Moon was called "Apollo," named after one of the most important gods in the Greek and Roman pantheon, the son of Zeus, the King of the gods. The Apollo spacecraft was actually two independent spacecraft, each designed around a basic principle: the humans onboard are an integral part of the "system." In contrast with the Soviet Union, NASA's spacecraft design philosophy has always been to make humans part of the control system for their spacecraft. From the very beginning, one of the central tenets of America's manned space program included the requirement that the astronauts onboard be able to operate and fly the spacecraft themselves. Unlike the Russians, whose spacecraft operated more or less automatically, American spacecraft were designed to have humans in the loop as integral parts of the spacecraft. This philosophy was reflected in the designs of America's manned spacecraft, beginning with our first one, the Mercury spacecraft. Mercury was built by the McDonnell-Douglas Aircraft Company and had manual controls for the astronaut onboard, which controlled the attitude (the direction it was pointed) and the ability to manually fire the retro rockets enabling the ship to return to Earth. Mercury's successor (also built by McDonnell Douglas) was the two-seater Gemini spacecraft. Gemini was a quantum leap in terms of the astronauts' ability to fly the spacecraft. Gemini astronauts could not only control its attitude, but could also control translation, movement up/down, right/left and forward/backward. These controls gave astronauts the capability to fly to, and dock with, other spacecraft in orbit. Gemini astronauts could even fly their spacecraft during atmospheric entry at the end of their mission. This capability was critical to the success of Apollo, since the technology of the day was only marginally capable (if at all) of supporting a completely automatic Moon landing, necessitating a significant role for the "man in the loop." In keeping with this philosophy, the Apollo spacecraft was even more of a pilot-controlled spacecraft than either Mercury or Gemini. This was especially true for the Lunar Module. The LM was unlike any other flying machine ever built, especially since it had to operate both in the zero gravity environment of orbital flight as well as in the Moon's low gravity (one sixth of the Earth's) as it descended to the lunar surface.

NASA's emphasis on man-in-the-loop spacecraft designs also influenced their selection criteria for the people to fly these spacecrafts. The first astronauts would be chosen from the ranks of military test pilots, men who had made careers of controlling exotic and groundbreaking aircraft. The first two groups of astronauts chosen all had such backgrounds. Eventually, the test pilot requirement would be dropped, and later still, non-pilot scientists and engineers would be chosen (something the Russians did almost from the beginning of their space program). But of all the men who landed lunar modules on the Moon, all but one was a military (or former military) test pilot. Neil Armstrong, who would be tasked with making the first Moon landing, was one of these. After a tour as a naval aviator in the Korean War, he had gone on to become a research engineer and test pilot for NASA. While most of the other astronauts were first and foremost pilots, who happened to have science or engineering degrees, Armstrong was a curious hybrid, as much engineer as he was pilot. James Hansen, the author of Armstrong's biography "First Man," quotes Armstrong, "While I was still in elementary school my intention was to be—or hope was to be—an aircraft designer. I later went into piloting because I thought a good designer ought to know the operational aspects of an airplane." Throughout his career, Armstrong would be known for his technical skill, his ability to absorb the engineering details of the aircraft or spacecraft he flew, and his ability to quickly and correctly analyze the most complex dynamic situations that arose during flight testing. Other pilots and astronauts might possess superior stick-and-rudder skills, but none were as adept as Armstrong at understanding the design and operation of the vehicles he flew.

Like Armstrong, Edwin "Buzz" Aldrin (who would accompany Armstrong as his copilot for the first Moon landing) possessed a deep and thorough knowledge of the details of spaceflight. He had earned a doctorate in astronautics from MIT and was one of only two Apollo astronauts who were both test pilots as well as PhD engineers. The title of Aldrin's doctoral dissertation was "Line of Sight Guidance Techniques for Manned Orbital Rendezvous." Aldrin was an experienced and accomplished pilot in his own right, but during Eagle's landing, he did not touch the controls. His job was to monitor Eagle's systems, keep track of altitude and velocity, and verbally provide Armstrong with all the information he needed to land. During Eagle's descent to the Moon, Aldrin carried out this role perfectly, dutifully reading off the data from Eagle's computer so that Armstrong could concentrate on flying the Lunar Module. He later said that for most of the descent, he never even looked out the window, but focused solely on monitoring and verbally relaying the data Armstrong needed. Together, he and Armstrong perfectly complemented each other, and the combination of their unique skills meshed seamlessly as they guided Eagle down to a landing on the Moon.

From the beginning of their flight training, pilots are trained to be ready for their aircraft to fail, and if it does, to respond in a way that ensures they survive. Thus, pilots tend to develop a strange relationship with their flying machines. On one hand they're willing to put their lives on the line, betting that their wings will stay on, that their engine will keep running, that their aircraft will safely carry them into the air and back to a gentle landing. On the other hand, they know that at any time, some failure could occur that puts them in mortal danger. Because of this, a great deal of their training involves what to do when these types of failures occur. Therefore, a good pilot tends to be a mixture of believer and skeptic, of optimist and pessimist. There was much about Eagle's landing that was still unknown, and more still that was merely uncertain; but Armstrong did all he could to stack the odds in his favor. A team of mission planners and systems experts developed an official set of rules to govern the flight, defining the parameters Eagle had to remain within to achieve a successful landing. However, behind the scenes Armstrong had his own ideas. He worked closely with his fellow NASA engineers to develop techniques he could use to independently keep track of how well Eagle was performing and how closely it was following the planned trajectory. He also did his own calculations to determine how close to the edge he could actually fly Eagle before being forced to call off the landing and initiate a complex and dangerous abort. His foresight was uncanny. By the time Eagle touched down on the Moon's "Sea of Tranquility," he had the opportunity to employ each one of these techniques and calculations.

The flight controllers in Mission Control had far more information available than did the astronauts onboard Eagle, and would play a critical role in getting Eagle safely down to the Moon. But their insight was limited because their only source of information was the data displayed on their console monitors. They were valuable advisers, remotely looking over the shoulders of the astronauts flying the Lunar Module, but as far as landing on the Moon, the astronauts would be on their own. The commander, as the sole operator of the Lunar Module's controls, would exercise all the privileges of the pilot-in–

command. In keeping with aviation tradition, he alone made the critical decision about whether to land or not. In aviation, the concept of the pilot in command is one of the most fundamental and sacrosanct traditions, and it carried over into the business of manned spaceflight. The underlying principle behind it is that the pilot is the best and final authority on what actions are required to ensure a safe and successful flight. As aviation matured and developed into a complex enterprise with multiple ground-based support facilities, especially in airline and military flight operations, conflicts inevitably arose as to who was the final authority during a flight. Was it the military commanders and corporate officers, the air traffic controllers, the engineering and maintenance teams, or the pilots? Eventually, in both military and civilian operations, the pilot was entrusted with the final authority on all decisions related to the safe and successful conduct of a flight. According to the International Civil Aviation Organization (ICAO), the governing body for international aircraft operations: "The pilot-in-command of an aircraft shall, whether manipulating the controls or not, be responsible for the operation of the aircraft in accordance with the rules of the air, except that the pilot-in-command may depart from these rules in circumstances that render such departure absolutely necessary in the interests of safety. The pilot-in-command of an aircraft shall have final authority as to the disposition of the aircraft while in command." Neil Armstrong heartily embraced his role as the pilot-in-command of Eagle, and from the moment he knew his crew would be tasked with attempting the first Moon landing, he began to assert his prerogative as the final authority on all matters pertaining to the job.

CHAPTER 2
Preparing for Landing

FIFTY THOUSAND FEET above the surface of the Moon, in a small, spindly spacecraft, two American astronauts— Neil Armstrong and Edwin "Buzz" Aldrin—prepare to initiate the computer program that would guide their spacecraft to a landing on a gently rolling plain about 250 miles away. Orbiting above them in the Command Module "Columbia," Michael Collins keeps a watchful eye over their activities. A little over 12 minutes later, according to the flight plan, Armstrong and Aldrin would become the first human beings to stand upon the surface of another world.

~~~~

Armstrong and Aldrin were firmly strapped into their Lunar Module, nicknamed "Eagle." They were not, however, strapped into their seats because they had no seats. In the all-consuming quest to reduce the weight of Eagle, all of which had to be supported by the 10,000 pounds of thrust generated by Eagle's descent engine, everything that was not absolutely essential was eliminated, including seats. So Armstrong and Aldrin were strapped down in a standing position by a system of pulleys and cables that allowed them to move just enough to reach critical switches and controls, while at the same time keeping them steady and secure enough to control the vehicle. It also let them press their helmets right up against the two small triangular shaped windows at the front of Eagle's cockpit. Windows are heavy, and although early concepts for the Lunar Module featured large, helicopter-like windows, it became apparent that these were also a luxury that was too heavy; they were replaced by much smaller and lighter weight windows. Thus, two weight-saving measures, eliminating both seats and large windows, complemented each other. If the astronauts were standing while flying the Lunar Module, then the small windows could be positioned close to their heads, giving them a much larger field of view.

The LM thus became the first flying machine flown from a standing position. All other flying machines had seats for the pilots, and were flown from a sitting position. Yet the very first flying machine, the Wright Flyer, also had no seats. The pilot flew it from a prone position, lying on his stomach. It was almost as if humans in flying machines had evolved from flying on their bellies to sitting upright to standing as they flew ever more advanced flying machines into the depths of space.

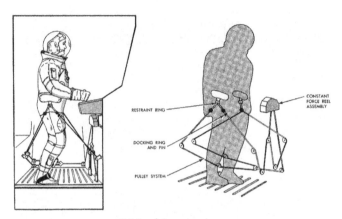

LM cable restraints

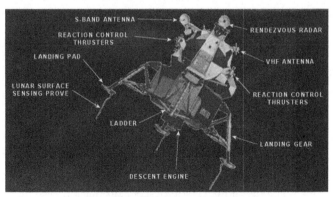

Details of the Lunar Module

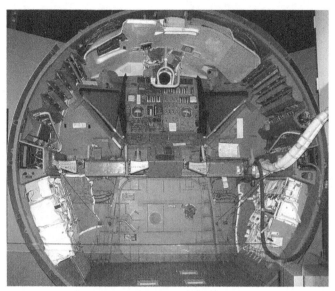

LM cockpit facing forward

After a two-year long give-and-take (and sometimes trial-and-error) design process for the Lunar Module, the final design that emerged was an ungainly, almost rickety looking thing that was unlike any other flying machine in history. However, since the Lunar Module did its flying in the airless vacuum of space, streamlining and smoothness were not required.

The LM was actually two spacecraft bolted together—an ascent stage where the crew resided, and an octagonal descent stage that housed the large, 10,000 pound thrust rocket engine known as the descent propulsion system, or DPS. The Lunar Module was also surprisingly small. With its legs extended, it stood only 22 feet 11 inches tall with a diameter of 31 feet measured diagonally between footpads.

As their names suggest, each Lunar Module stage had a specific function: the descent stage facilitated the descent to and landing on the Moon and also served as the launch pad for the ascent stage. The ascent stage carried Armstrong and Aldrin back into orbit to rejoin Columbia. It also served as a combined cockpit (from which Armstrong and Aldrin controlled Eagle), a sleeping compartment, bathroom and storage space. The interior of the ascent stage, where Armstrong and Aldrin remained except for the short time they spent walking on the Moon, was shaped somewhat like two tuna cans joined together, one slightly larger than the other. Astronauts flew the Lunar Module from the front "can," which was about six feet in diameter and about three feet long. It contained the windows, the controls and displays, and the hatch they used to exit to the lunar surface. The back can, about four

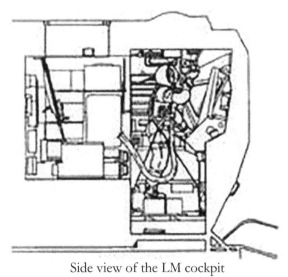

Side view of the LM cockpit

feet in diameter and five feet long, housed the electronics and life support equipment, as well as the ascent engine, on which their lives literally depended. The engine was covered with a cylindrical cover about the size of a garbage can. Two hammocks were provided for the astronauts to sleep in. Altogether, the interior provided about 160 cubic feet of living space, about the same as a typical minivan.

The ascent stage contained all the life support equipment required to keep the crew alive, and also the controls and displays to allow them to fly the LM down to a soft landing on the Moon. It also had four sets of four small rocket thrusters—called "quads"—to control the LM's attitude. The descent stage housed the DPS, which at the time was the most advanced rocket engine in history. It could be throttled down to a thrust level of only 10 percent (about 1000 pounds), something that no other rocket engine had the capability to do. Before the development of the DPS engine, all rocket engines were binary, i.e., they were either off or they were operating at full thrust. Landing on the Moon, however, required a rocket engine that could be throttled down so that the LM could settle gently onto the Moon. The mechanism used to throttle the descent engine was a "pintle injector" (a pintle is a long, thin, cylindrical object) with a hollow pintle, through which the rocket propellant flowed into the combustion chamber. The pintle was surrounded by a movable sleeve that could be used to vary the engine thrust level. Even though it represented the pinnacle of rocket technology at the time, the concept was rather simple. Almost everyone is familiar with it because the same concept is used in a garden hose sprayer. A typical sprayer uses a movable sleeve and pintle, which can vary the water stream from a narrow, high thrust stream to a wide, fan-shaped, low thrust stream. The descent stage also had four large legs to facilitate a gentle landing on the Moon. The legs had a crushable honeycomb material inside them that was specially developed for the LM. This material allowed engineers to avoid the use of heavy and complicated hydraulic cylinders. At the bottom of each leg a three-foot wide footpad was attached. The footpads distributed the weight of the LM across a larger area and also allowed the LM to slide along the lunar surface when landing. Three of the footpads also had a five-and-a-half-foot rod with a contact sensor at the end. Once two of these probes contacted the Moon's surface, a blue landing light would illuminate on the LM's center control panel so that the crew would know they had landed. Once the light was lit, the commander was trained to delay for about a second, and then shut off the descent engine, allowing the LM to fall the remaining five feet or so to the lunar surface. Under the Moon's low gravity—only about one-sixth of the Earth's—the LM would settle to the surface in a leisurely two seconds or so. The LM's designers thought it was important to turn off the engine before the LM settled completely on the Moon. Otherwise, they worried that its exhaust could reflect off the surface and damage the bottom of the LM. Their fears were overstated, as Armstrong soon proved.

The LM looked remarkably like a mutant insect—with four legs instead of six, a smattering of antennae growing at odd angles and locations, an asymmetrical head that bulged on one side and was relatively flat on the other, and two eyes canted downward and slanted as if in a perpetual squint. It was not, by any aeronautical standard, pretty. In fact, it was downright ugly. In the weeks leading up to the first Moon landing, the Volkswagen automobile company took out full page ads in prominent magazines and newspapers featuring a model of a Lunar Module along with the Volkswagen logo and the statement "It's ugly, but it gets you there." Volkswagen produced their own bug-like machine, the Beetle, and they obviously saw a kinship between the two aesthetically challenged but highly functional machines.

While Armstrong and Aldrin were the on the Moon, their crewmate Michael Collins was flying solo in the Columbia. Much had been made in the press about his isolation; NASA's own public relations staff pointed out that, at the time, he was "the most isolated human being since Adam." His isolation was real, especially during the 45 minutes during each two-hour-long Moon orbit when he was on the Moon's far side and out of radio contact with Earth. Years later, in the era of internet memes, one featured the iconic photo Collins took of Eagle as she returned to lunar orbit after the landing, with the Earth in the background. The meme points out that every human alive, including the two who just walked on the Moon, is in the photograph except for Collins. The hype about his loneliness made for an interesting sideline to the main story, but Collins apparently had no concerns. In fact, he seemed to look forward to it. He did, however, carry one burden that weighed heavily on him until the three crewmembers were reunited in the Columbia. If for some reason Eagle would have been unable to lift off from the Moon, he would have had the awful responsibility of leaving Armstrong and Aldrin behind and returning to Earth alone. This was such a real possibility that President Nixon had tasked his press secretary, Bill Safire, with writing a letter that he would read to the nation on live television should Armstrong and Aldrin be stranded on the Moon. The letter began "IN THE EVENT OF MOON DISASTER: Fate has ordained that the men who went to the Moon to explore in peace will stay on the Moon to 'rest in peace'." Several paragraphs later, the letter concluded with the statement "A clergyman should adopt the same procedure as a burial at sea, commending their souls to the 'deepest of the deep' and concluding with the Lord's Prayer."

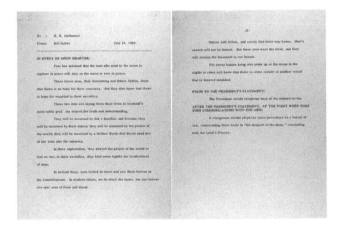

The only human, alive or dead, not contained
within the frame of this photo is Michael Collins.
The ultimate anti-selfie. Apollo 11.

CHAPTER 3
Ready for Landing

NEIL ARMSTRONG AND Edwin *"Buzz" Aldrin*
are making the final preparations for the first landing on the Moon.
It's Sunday, July 20, 1969. About five minutes past 4:00 PM
Eastern Standard Time. The date and time are not arbitrary—
rather, they have been carefully chosen by mission planners to ensure
that the Sun is behind Eagle and at just the right height above the
Lunar horizon to provide good shadows. Otherwise, during final
approach Armstrong might have a very difficult time visually judging
his height above the Moon's surface, which is devoid of trees, buildings
and other objects that provide visual cues to Earthly pilots.

Mission Control (in Houston, Texas) has given the crew of
Apollo 11 a "go" to begin the descent to the Moon's surface. It will
take about 12 minutes, depending upon how long Armstrong takes
to reconnoiter the landing site. For NASA, barely a decade old, this
will be the most critical twelve minutes in its young history. For the
last 8 years, since President Kennedy committed the United States to
" ... achieving the goal, before this decade is out, of landing a man on

the Moon and returning him safely to the Earth," NASA's army of over 400,000 civil servants, contractors and military personnel have worked tirelessly to reach this point. They have devoted practically every waking minute of their lives to this goal. It has cost some their health; others their marriages. It has cost some their lives. Now the goal is within reach. In about the time it takes a person to walk a mile at a brisk pace, they will know if their sacrifice has been fruitful. Or if it has been in vain.

~~~~

Up to this point, everything that the crew of Apollo 11 had experienced had been done before, but nothing like the events of those upcoming twelve minutes had ever been attempted. The launch onboard the most powerful rocket ever built, the mighty Saturn V, the three-day coast from the Earth to the Moon, entering the 60–mile-high orbit around the Moon, and even Descent Orbit Insertion (DOI), which took them down to an orbit barely 10 miles above the Moon's surface, had all been done before. Even the lift off and ascent from the Moon, when the upper part of the Lunar Module would blast off from the lunar surface, had been simulated in both Earth orbit (on Apollo 9) and lunar orbit (on Apollo 10). But the final descent down to the surface of the Moon, which comprised just a little over 12 minutes of the total mission time of eight days and four hours, had never been simulated during actual spaceflight. NASA had launched 20 rockets carrying humans into space. They had docked two spacecraft together on seven different occasions. American astronauts had ventured outside their spacecraft into the harsh, threatening vacuum of space ten times. They had flown Lunar Modules twice, once in Earth orbit and once orbiting around the Moon. But no one had ever flown a spacecraft from an orbit around a planet down to a landing. Even spacecraft returning to Earth had previously landed by parachute with astronauts and cosmonauts sitting passively in their spacecraft. The short descent to the lunar surface was truly undiscovered country. Uncertainty prevailed as the world awaited those all-important 12 minutes.

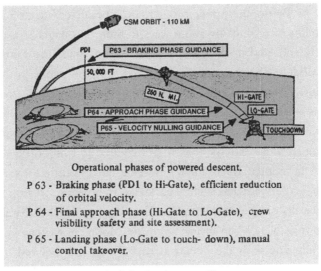

Operational phases of powered descent.

P 63 - Braking phase (PD1 to Hi-Gate), efficient reduction of orbital velocity.

P 64 - Final approach phase (Hi-Gate to Lo-Gate), crew visibility (safety and site assessment).

P 65 - Landing phase (Lo-Gate to touch- down), manual control takeover.

Eagle's descent profile

Of course, attempting any new spaceflight operation without simulating it first was anathema to NASA's team of Apollo engineers. So a variety of methods, none entirely satisfactory—were employed in an attempt to give the astronauts at least an inkling of what it would be like to land a spindly and ungainly vehicle like the LM on the surface of a world where everything weighed one-sixth of its Earth weight. Helicopters were the first thought, and indeed every lunar landing crew did train in helicopters, but they were not a very good analog for a lunar module. Instead, the task of training astronauts for the final few hundred feet of the Moon landing fell to an incredibly dangerous flying machine that NASA itself described as "unconventional, contrary and ugly." It was officially known as the Lunar Landing Training Vehicle or "LLTV."

Before the Apollo program even began, engineers and pilots were thinking about ways to train astronauts how to fly and land a spacecraft on the Moon. Since the Lunar Modules themselves were designed only to operate in the lower gravity of the Moon, they couldn't be used to train astronauts on Earth. And because of the reduced gravity of the Moon, the maneuvers required for landing were much more extreme than those required to land on Earth. A helicopter, for example, must be tilted slightly forward to go forward and slightly backward to go back. This tilt is usually on the order of about five degrees, which is barely noticeable. When flying over the Moon, however, with only one-sixth the gravity of the Earth, the required tilt would be six times as much—or nearly 30 degrees! Thus, the first and most obvious choice for training future Moon-landing astronauts—a helicopter—would not be useful at all. The types of maneuvers required simply couldn't be performed by a helicopter. Although helicopters would eventually be added into the training curriculum, mainly to familiarize astronauts with vertical flight, some other kind of flying machine would be required if the astronauts were to be trained in the realities of lunar landings. In 1960, before NASA had any formal plans to fly to the Moon, some pilots and engineers at the Flight Research Center at Edwards Air Force Base had begun to think about how pilots could fly a spacecraft down to a Moon landing and how they could be trained to do it. This was a very difficult problem, greatly complicated by the Moon's lower gravity. What was needed was a flying machine that could land vertically while also counteracting five-sixths of its weight so that it could fly and maneuver just as it would in the Moon's low gravity. Two flight research center engineers, Gene Matranga and Don Bellman, with the assistance of a young NASA test pilot, Neil Armstrong, came up with a preliminary design for a lunar-landing training vehicle which, according to Armstrong, looked remarkably like a "tin ... can with four legs."

Thus was born the Lunar Landing Research Vehicle (LLRV) and its more advanced cousin, the Lunar Landing Training Vehicle (LLTV). Two LLRVs were built, and they played an important role in refining the design of the Lunar Module, especially in developing the handling qualities that would allow an astronaut to safely fly down for a manual landing. They were also used to evaluate the optimum cockpit design (the size and location of flight displays and hand controllers) for the Lunar Module. One concession was made; instead of the pilot standing as in the Lunar Module, the LLRV and LLTV had ejection seats, a nod to the fact that these were very novel and potentially dangerous flying machines. This would prove to be a very fortuitous decision, as one LLRV and two LLTVs would crash during the lifetime of the Program (A loss rate of 50 percent!). Yet, in each case, the pilots survived. One of them was Neil Armstrong. In May of 1968, just a little over a year before his Apollo 11 mission, Armstrong was flying LLRV Number 1 at Ellington Air Force Base in Houston. During a practice lunar landing, Armstrong had descended to about 30 feet when the rocket engines started to fail, causing the LLRV to descend faster. Armstrong switched modes to compensate, and the LLRV started to climb, but then ran out of fuel for its attitude control rockets and spun out of control. As it nosed up and rolled over at an altitude of only 200 feet, Armstrong ejected and parachuted safely down. LLRV-1 crashed and was destroyed.

The LLRV and LLTV were unlike any Earthly flying machines in the history of flight. More than anything else they resembled old-fashioned metal bed frames that had magically developed the ability to fly. In fact, pilots nicknamed them "Flying Bedsteads," and they flew like you might expect a flying bed to fly. Yet, to a person, every single Apollo commander who landed a Lunar Module on the Moon said the training provided by the LLTVs was absolutely essential in acquiring the ability to manually land a Lunar Module on the Moon.

LLTV

CHAPTER 4

Thirteen Minutes to Landing

ARMSTRONG AND ALDRIN are now less than a minute away from starting their descent to the Lunar surface. In the minutes leading up to Powered Descent Initiation (PDI), when Eagle's descent engine is ignited to begin the "braking phase"— literally slowing Eagle down so that it falls out of orbit and begins its long descent to the Moon's surface—a series of communications problems between Eagle and Mission Control have bedeviled the astronauts and their counterparts in Mission Control. In fact, these problems are serious enough that Flight Director, Gene Kranz, is worried about having to terminate the landing. Eagle's landing is a complex, tightly planned operation that depends upon the close interaction— and communication—between the Lunar Module and Mission Control. So good communications are essential. Eagle is now 50,000 feet above the Moon, just a little higher than a typical commercial airliner flies. However, it's traveling at 3400 miles per hour, about seven times that of a typical airliner. Things happen quickly at such speeds, and there's very little margin for slow reaction times on the part of the crew. They are ready to begin the first phase of the descent to the Moon's surface, the braking phase, when they fire the LM's big rocket motor to slow it down, to "brake" them out of their orbit around the Moon. At this point, Armstrong and Aldrin are "flying" Eagle mainly by making inputs to Eagle's computer, formally named the Apollo Guidance Computer or AGC.

~~~~

The AGC was a marvel of 1960s era technology. Its basic architecture was far different from the computers that would be an integral part of our lives in the 21st century. Its paltry memory, far less than the eventual smart phone, was contained in an iron "core" that had a multitude of holes drilled through it. Copper wires were threaded throughout these holes in a complex pattern which, when magnetized by passing an electrical current through the wires, created memory registers that could be programmed to enable Eagle to carry out every activity required to accomplish a landing on the Moon and also a launch back into Lunar orbit. The routing pattern for the copper wires was determined by the brilliant young programmers at MIT's famed Instrumentation Laboratory. These wire programs constituted the "software" for Eagle's computer, and once the program was written, it was loaded into the computer by an army of "little old ladies," known as "LOLs." Each of the LOLs was an expert seamstress prior to joining the Apollo effort, and they literally weaved the program into the computer by threading the copper wires through the matrix of holes in the pattern specified by the programmers.

LM computer

The "software" for the LM computer

CHAPTER 5
The Descent Begins

EAGLE'S BIG DESCENT engine starts automatically under the control of the computer. Armstrong calls down "Ignition" to Mission Control. Initially, the thrust is set at only 10 percent of its maximum thrust to allow Eagle's computer to position the engine's nozzle so that the engine is thrusting precisely through Eagle's center of mass. This is critical since Eagle is flying entirely under rocket power, without any aerodynamic forces to help stabilize it. In effect, it's balanced on top of its rocket engine's thrust plume, similar to having a broom vertically balanced on the palm of your hand. It takes 26 seconds for Eagle's computer to properly find the correct direction to point the engine's nozzle and to verify it can maintain this direction. Right on time, as Aldrin counts up, "24, 25, 26," the computer commands the engine, via a software subroutine named "Burn Baby Burn" by the programmers, to throttle up to its full thrust level of 10,500 pounds. "Throttle up. Looks good!" Aldrin reports.

At the same time the computer is working to find the right nozzle position to keep Eagle in balance, it is also monitoring

Eagle's position over the Moon's surface and calculating the right time to accelerate to full thrust so that the descent to landing would end directly over the planned landing site. Like any good pilot, Armstrong is closely monitoring Eagle's position to make sure the computer is taking Eagle to the right landing spot. Within a few minutes, he would realize it was not.

CHAPTER 6

Twelve Minutes to Landing

ONE MINUTE AFTER Eagle's rocket engine starts up for the long descent to the Moon's surface, communications problems arise again. Mission Control loses contact with Eagle, but not Columbia, orbiting 50 miles above Eagle. Astronaut Charlie Duke, an Air Force major and former test pilot serving as the CapCom (Capsule Communicator), the only person in Mission Control who is authorized to speak directly to the astronauts in space, asks Mike Collins to relay a message to Eagle: "Tell them to go aft Omni. Over." Mission Control hopes that switching to a multi-directional antenna at the top rear of Eagle's ascent stage will enable them to regain communication with Eagle. If Mission Control and Eagle can't communicate, the landing will have to be called off. The task of landing on the Moon is so complex, requiring the combined systems monitoring capability and skill of everyone in Mission Control, as well as Armstrong and Aldrin, that it simply can't be accomplished if they can't communicate with each other.

Fortunately, Collins is still in contact with Eagle, and he relays Mission Control's request. Aldrin, however, is already implementing his own solution. Turning to the instrument panel on his right, he begins manually "slewing" Eagle's big S-band antenna, searching for the right direction that will enable Eagle to regain the signal from Mission Control. "OK, see if they read me now," he asks Collins. Aldrin's plan works, and soon Eagle and Mission Control are communicating with each other again. Another crisis is averted, and Eagle continues her descent to the Moon. But their troubles aren't over, and soon Armstrong and Aldrin have to deal with several problems that threaten a successful landing.

"Rate of descent looks good," Aldrin tells Armstrong.

CHAPTER 7

Eleven Minutes to Landing

ALDRIN REPORTS THAT the "AGS and PGNS agree very closely."

~~~~

Eagle had two guidance systems to tell it where it was and where it was going—the Primary Guidance and Navigation System (PGNS, pronounced "pings") and the Abort Guidance System (AGS, pronounced "ags"). As its name suggests, the PGNS was the primary guidance system. It was one of the most technically advanced and complex systems onboard Eagle, consisting primarily of three gyroscopes, which measured the orientation of the Lunar Module, and three accelerometers, used to measure acceleration, which could then be used to determine the velocity of the Lunar Module in different directions. These were all mounted within a solid block of beryllium metal and contained inside a metal sphere about the size of a basketball. The entire assembly, known as the Inertial Measurement Unit (IMU), transmitted its precious guidance and navigation information to Eagle's computer, where it was used to generate information used by the computer and the crew to fly Eagle. The Apollo IMU was built by the Delco Division of the General Motors Corporation, just one example of how the Apollo Program enlisted the services of a multitude of American industries and corporations, not just the traditional big aerospace companies.

The AGS was a less-capable version of the PGNS, designed to take over in case of a failure in the primary system. It could guide Eagle safely back up to orbit in the case of an abort, but it couldn't guide Eagle down to a landing. Since the AGS had to be ready to take over at a moment's notice, Aldrin kept a close eye on it to ensure that the guidance and navigation information was consistent with the PGNS. Fortunately it was, as Aldrin reported to Armstrong and Mission Control.

CHAPTER 8
Ten Minutes to Landing

ARMSTRONG ASKS ALDRIN, "Want to get rid *of this radar?" referring to the rendezvous radar to which Aldrin replies, "Yeah." In response, Armstrong flips a switch to put Eagle's rendezvous radar in the SLEW position. This tells the computer to operate the radar in a mode which has it continually tracking Columbia, orbiting high above Eagle. This adds a measure of safety since the rendezvous radar will now be ready to immediately start leading Eagle back to a quick rendezvous with Columbia should an abort be required. A few minutes later, this routine action leads to a series of computer overload messages—called "program alarms"— that almost causes an abort. It's a perfect example of how exacting and unforgiving spaceflight can be.*

~~~~

Special electronic components in the radar and the computer were designed to keep in phase with each other, so the computer always knew which way the radar was pointing, but an unknown design flaw caused them to occasionally be out of phase. Incredibly, Armstrong flipped the radar switch at the precise moment when these components were out of phase, and from that point on the computer was confused about where to point the radar. This confusion caused literally millions of pointing commands to be issued by the computer as it tried to point the radar to the correct location. The commands overloaded Eagle's computer and caused it to annunciate the program alarms.

Five of these alarms, known as "1201" and "1202" alarms, would occur throughout Eagle's landing approach, and each alarm triggered a reboot of the computer. The alarms were caused by an "executive overload," computerese for a computer that is being asked to do too much and can't complete all the tasks assigned to it. Unfortunately, the computer technology available to the Eagle had a very limited memory capacity. Fortunately, the computer engineers at MIT's Instrumentation Laboratory who programmed the computers envisioned such a situation and wrote the software in such a way that it automatically prioritized each task it is performing. So during a critical operation—like landing on the Moon—the computer would not perform lower priority tasks; instead, it focused on those tasks that were vitally important.

~~~~

*A few seconds later, Armstrong ominously comments to Aldrin, "...
we went by the three-minute point early. We're going to land long."
Aldrin doesn't respond; perhaps he didn't hear Armstrong, or he's
focused on other data, because he incongruously responds back, "rate
of descent is looking real good. Altitude's about right on." Still focused on their landing path, Armstrong then reports to Houston,
"Our position checks down range show us to be a little long."*

~~~~

Armstrong had no special display or instruments to warn
him of Eagle's departure from its planned flight path. Rather, he was using a grid etched into the commander's
window to estimate how fast Eagle is moving over the
ground. This grid, which consisted of a series of lines
spaced two degrees apart, was designed to be used during
Eagle's final approach to the surface to tell the commander
where on the surface the computer was targeting to land
the LM. Known as the "Landing Point Designator" or
"LPD," the grid was used in conjunction with an angle
calculated and displayed by the computer. During landing,
the LM Pilot would read this angle from the computer
display and verbally report it to the commander, who
would then look at the line on the window's LPD grid cor-
responding to that angle. The point on the Moon directly
under that LPD line would be the landing site. The commander could then decide if that site was acceptable, and if
not, he could change it by toggling a switch on his control
panel to command Eagle's computer to target a different
landing site. Armstrong realized during his pre-flight train-

ing that the LPD scale could also be used to time how fast (in degrees/per second) Eagle was moving over landmarks on the ground. That information would tell him whether Eagle was going to land at the planned landing site, or before or beyond it.

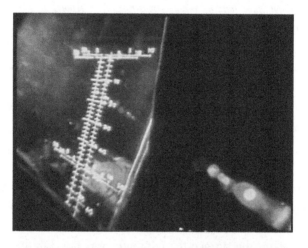

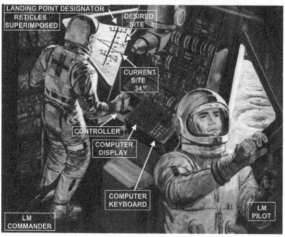

Landing point designators

Determining Eagle's approach path to its planned landing site was a very difficult navigational problem, and there were several interrelated factors that contributed to the difficulty. Chief among these was the poor understanding of the Moon's gravitational field. Unlike atmospheric flight over the Earth, where the major contributor to navigational errors is winds aloft, flight over the lunar surface is governed by the Moon's gravity. Unfortunately, the Moon's gravity is non-uniform and prone to large variations depending upon location. These variations were largely due to something called mass concentrations, or "mascons."

No one knew (or knows today) the origin of the mascons. The best guess is that they are the remnants of large rocky objects that impacted the Moon with enough energy to burrow into the Moon's mantle and cause local increases in density, and hence, a gravitational anomaly. Whatever they were, they made it very difficult to model the Moon's gravity field in the computer. And without an accurate gravity model, the computer couldn't accurately display Eagle's altitude. Armstrong was deeply concerned about this inaccuracy. Knowing the altitude above the surface is the most fundamental and vital piece of information a pilot needs. A few months before flight, Armstrong got together with an engineer at the Manned Spacecraft Center in Houston, and using what Armstrong called "barnyard math," they developed a technique to calculate Eagle's altitude. Using a stopwatch, Armstrong could time how long it took for a landmark on the Moon to pass some predetermined number of degrees on the LPD grid. This would be a direct measure of Eagle's angular rate, a quantity typically called "omega." There's a mathematical relationship that relates omega to velocity and altitude, specifically, altitude can be found by dividing velocity by omega. Armstrong and a few other NASA engineers also developed a graph that plotted their orbital velocity, altitude and omega. Their orbital velocity was very well known, since accelerometers onboard Eagle and radar from the Earth could both measure it very accurately. Using the value for omega that he measured, Armstrong could compare it to the graph and determine their current altitude. Thus, the crew had a pretty good idea of their altitude even if, as was commonly the case, the altitude as determined by the computer's guidance software was way off.

In order to use Armstrong's special technique to track Eagle's descent, the LM was oriented to a face-down position—with its windows facing the Moon's surface—during the early part of its descent. This allowed Armstrong to survey the Lunar surface and monitor their approach path. Eagle's descent profile was originally designed to be flown face-up the entire time, until the pitch down maneuver that was planned for just before touchdown to give the crew a view of their landing site. But Armstrong had requested that he and Aldrin fly face down for the beginning phases of the descent for landing, so that he could track their ground track during the early part of Eagle's descent to the Moon. No other Moon landing would use this technique, but Armstrong insisted on it for the first landing.

CHAPTER 9
Nine Minutes to Landing

A LITTLE OVER three minutes into the descent, Aldrin reports, "Altitude rate looks right down the groove." Armstrong however, still concerned about their ground track, comments "Roger. About three seconds long," meaning that Eagle is about three seconds ahead of where it should be at this point in its descent. At Eagle's current velocity of nearly 3600 miles per hour, this translates to a landing about three miles "long." In other words, Eagle was heading for a touchdown three miles away from the planned site. With all other unknowns facing Eagle and her crew, this could be disastrous!

~~~~

Incredibly, Armstrong's "barnyard" technique for determining Eagle's altitude alerted him to the discrepancy in Eagle's planned flight path down to the surface. Although Armstrong's entire professional career had involved test flying aircraft at the cutting edges of aeronautical science, his work helping to develop techniques to better monitor Eagle's descent from orbit proved that he was as talented an engineer as he was a pilot. Armstrong was always fond of pointing out that he was an engineer at heart, and he must have relished the opportunity to flex his "engineering muscles" a little in the months leading up to the first Moon landing.

~~~~

A few seconds later Armstrong rolls Eagle over on its back, 180 degrees away from its current position. Now its windows are facing up, away from the lunar surface, and the crew can no longer see the ground below them. Armstrong notices that Eagle's roll rate is much slower than anticipated. "Boy I tell you, this is much harder to do than it was ..." Armstrong comments. "Keep it going," Aldrin urges him. Armstrong quickly diagnoses the problem:—A switch that sets Eagle's roll rate is in the wrong position, causing it to rotate at only five degrees per second, five times slower than planned. Armstrong places the switch in the "25 degrees per second" position, and Eagle quickly rolls to its face-up position. Because of the delay in getting to the face-up attitude, Eagle's landing radar, located at the bottom of the descent stage and unable to view the Moon's surface until Eagle is in a face-up position, failed to lock onto the surface when originally planned. Instead, lock on doesn't occur until Eagle is down to about 40,000 feet, nearly 2000 feet lower than expected. The landing radar is absolutely essential if Eagle is to make a successful landing. It's the only way to get a truly accurate reading of Eagle's height above the surface, and without it, Armstrong and Aldrin are essentially "flying blind."

~~~~

Like its computer, Eagle's landing radar was a marvel of sixties era technology, and far more advanced than the type typically used in aircraft of the time. Using four separate radar beams, the radar operated by using the Doppler Effect to determine its altitude and its forward and sideways velocity. It was essentially a space-rated, high-tech version of the types of radars that police use today to catch speeders. The Doppler Effect, named after Christian Doppler, the Austrian physicist who first described it, occurs when radio waves or sound waves are emanated from or bounced off a moving object. The waves are either compressed or stretched depending upon whether the object is moving toward or away from the antenna. The compression or stretching of the waves changes the signal's frequency, which can be used to calculate both the distance to, and the speed of, the object. The classic illustration of the Doppler Effect is the changing pitch of a train horn as it approaches and then moves away from you.

The landing radar was designed and built by the Ryan Aeronautical Corporation. By 1969, Ryan had transitioned from building airplanes to building sophisticated electronic devices like Eagle's radar. But over forty years ago, Ryan built one of the most famous aircraft of all time, Charles Lindbergh's iconic "Spirit of St. Louis." In 1927, Lindbergh, to whom Armstrong was often compared, flew the Spirit of St. Louis on the first solo, non-stop flight across the Atlantic Ocean, from New York to Paris. Unlike

Lindbergh, who made his 33-hour flight completely alone
and out of contact with anyone on the ground, Armstrong
was supported by a vast army of engineers and scientists
with whom he was in constant radio contact. But in the
final minutes of the landing, as Eagle's fuel level steadily
dropped and he desperately searched for a smooth spot to
land. Armstrong must have felt just as alone as Lindbergh.

~~~~

*Eagle has now been descending toward the Moon for four minutes.
The LM Timeline Book calls for a check of Eagle's explosive device
(ED) batteries.*

~~~~

Spaceflight pioneered the use of explosive devices, also
called "pyrotechnic fasteners" or "explosive attachment
devices," as fasteners for hardware that needed to remain
attached during some phase of flight, but that would have to
be separated later. Most commonly manifested as exploding
nuts and bolts, pyrotechnic fasteners were absolutely
essential to the operation of all spacecraft, whether manned
or unmanned. They were necessary for attaching rocket
stages together—and for ensuring that they separated
quickly when required. Pyrotechnic bolts held rockets down
on their launch pads and released them for their long climb
toward space. They also powered "guillotine" devices,
which sliced electrical cables between rocket stages and
spacecraft modules when it was time for them to separate.

Batteries were critical to the operation of Eagle's pyrotechnic devices, without which Eagle's ascent stage couldn't separate from the descent stage in case of an abort, or when ascending from the lunar surface after a successful landing. If the batteries did not function properly, a safe landing would be impossible.

~~~~

Aldrin performs the checks and reports, "Okay, Houston, the ED batts are GO ... at four minutes," to which CapCom Charlie Duke replies "Roger. You are Go. You are Go to continue powered descent. You are Go to continue powered descent."

CHAPTER 10
Eight Minutes to Landing

EAGLE IS EIGHT *minutes from landing, and once again communications problems arise. CapCom Charlie Duke reports to the Apollo 11 crew: "We've got data dropout. You're still looking good." The communications problems have not become serious enough to require an abort, but they are becoming a significant distraction to Armstrong and Aldrin. Aldrin's primary task is to monitor Eagle's computer and other instruments, so that Armstrong can focus on the task of flying the Lunar Module and looking for a suitable landing site. But Aldrin finds himself spending so much time and effort with the communications problems that he's having trouble keeping an eye on Eagle's other systems. In fact, he's manually pointing the big S-band antenna, something that was never practiced during the pre-flight simulations. He wonders whether Eagle is still being monitored by Mission Control, or whether he and Armstrong are on their own and will have to try to land without any help from Houston. Despite the nagging communications problems, all appears to be well. But that's about to change, and the next seven minutes will be as hair-raising a time as NASA has ever experienced.*

Armstrong is concerned enough about the communications problems that he queries Aldrin, "How do you look over there?" Aldrin replies, "Okay." Then, after a long pause he reports, "Okay, we got good landing radar lock on." "We got a lock on?" Armstrong asks seemingly surprised. "Yeah," says Aldrin, altitude light's out, Delta H is minus 2900."

"Delta H is minus 2900." In the engineering-speak that NASA typically uses, Aldrin is reporting that the difference in height (Delta H), as measured by the landing radar, is 2900 feet lower than what Eagle's computer is calculating. Although quite a large difference, at this point in the descent it's within the acceptable limits so it's of no concern. Mission Control and Aldrin continue to closely watch the Delta H for the next several minutes to ensure it decreases to an acceptable number. Since the landing radar is performing as expected, producing good radar reflections from the Moon's surface, the altitude light on Eagle's computer display has gone out.

Just minutes ago, Armstrong had rolled Eagle to the right, rotating around a line that runs straight through the center of the rocket engine's exhaust plume. Until that point, Armstrong and Aldrin had been flying with their faces down toward the Moon. Now they are face up, with the soles of their feet pointing in the direction of flight and their backs pointing down toward the lunar surface, less than 40,000 feet below. A brilliant blue Earth shines straight ahead through their windows, a scene that has, remarkably, become familiar to humans after only three missions to the Moon. Aldrin reports that he's "got the Earth straight out our front window. "Sure do," Armstrong replies, then, says to Mission Control, "Houston, I hope

you're looking at our Delta H." "That's affirmative," CapCom
Charlie Duke reassures him.

~~~~

Armstrong's concern about Eagle's altitude, and the inher-
ent uncertainty in measuring it, played a significant role in
his piloting strategy. Measuring an airplane's altitude is a
simple and straightforward matter; one simply measures
the outside air pressure, which drops with altitude at a predictable rate. From the earliest days of aviation, aircraft
have employed barometers (commonly used by meteorol-
ogists to measure air pressure) modified especially for aeri-
al use and called altimeters. But the Moon's airless environment renders aircraft altimeters unusable, so engineers
had to come up with another method for measuring a
spacecraft's altitude. Unfortunately, because of the
Mascons, it was notoriously difficult to measure altitude
above the Moon.

~~~~

Their propellant is half depleted now, with about 50 percent remain-
ing in the tanks. With more empty space in the propellant tanks, the
fluids begin to slosh around causing Eagle to wobble like a top as it
slows down. The motion is enough to cause Eagle's computer to com-
mand its rocket thrusters to fire several times in an attempt to damp-
en the motion. This is unexpected, as it was never simulated during
pre-flight training, and Armstrong is surprised.

~~~~

The sloshing motion peaked out around eight minutes before landing, but it persisted at a lesser magnitude throughout the entire landing. As Eagle neared its landing site, the motion hampered the operation of the Landing Point Designator (LPD) to the point that Armstrong would eventually choose not to use it at all (especially when subsequent computer alarms caused him to doubt the reliability of the computer as well, since the computer was providing the data required to use the LPD). Even more seriously, the sloshing motion of the propellant causes the low propellant sensor to illuminate 30 seconds early, adding to a cascading chain of events that threatened to overwhelm both Mission Control and Eagle's crew.

Armstrong had little time to dwell on this, however, as another problem surfaced, one so serious that Flight Director Gene Kranz contemplated aborting the landing.

~~~~

"Program alarm," Armstrong reports to Mission Control. "It's a 1202." There's a distinct hint of concern in Armstrong's normally laconic voice tone. Eagle is at an altitude of 33,500 feet, just under eight minutes from landing.

CHAPTER 11

Seven Minutes to Landing

ARMSTRONG TURNS TO Aldrin and asks "What is it?" He is referring to the 1202 alarm. Aldrin is puzzled as well—this is not an alarm they've encountered in their training. Five of these alarms—known as "1201" and "1202" alarms—will occur throughout Eagle's landing approach, and each alarm triggers a reboot of the computer. The alarms are caused by an "executive overload," computerese for a computer that is being asked to do too much, and can't complete all the tasks assigned to it. Unfortunately, the computer technology available at the time only allowed for a very limited memory capacity for Eagle's computer. Fortunately, the MIT engineers envisioned such a situation and wrote the software in such a way that it automatically prioritized each task it was performing. So during a critical operation—like landing on the Moon—the computer would simply not perform the lower priority tasks, and focus instead on those tasks that were vitally important.

Armstrong then keys his microphone to enable him to talk to Houston. "Give us a reading on the 1202 Program Alarm." His tone is curt and expectant—he wants an answer now. Two young flight controllers working together in Mission Control—Steve Bales and Jack Garman—determine that the alarm is due to the computer being overloaded, and they know that the computer will continue to function, while ignoring the tasks that are not critical to the landing. They tell Flight Director Kranz that the landing is still "Go," and Duke relays this good news to Armstrong and Aldrin." You are Go to continue powered descent" he tells them. For emphasis he repeats himself—" You are Go to continue powered descent."

~~~~

During a simulated landing a few weeks prior to the launch of Apollo 11, the Mission Control team had called an abort for a similar alarm, primarily because none of the flight controllers were familiar with the alarm and what—if any—impacts it would have on the landing. Fortunately, flight director Gene Kranz ordered an exhaustive review of all the program alarms written into the software. Flight controller Jack Garman subsequently prepared a handwritten list of each alarm and its consequences. When the alarms occurred, he referred to his list and informed his fellow flight controller Steve Bales that there was no need to abort. Bales quickly relayed to Flight Director Kranz—using the crisp and efficient vernacular of Mission Control—that they were still "Go." There was no reason to call off the landing.

Much has been written about the coolness under extreme pressure that Bales and Garman displayed, but the MIT engineers deserve a lot of credit as well. Their clever

programming allowed the computer to continue function-
ing normally giving Armstrong confidence that he could
proceed with the landing. As Armstrong would later relate
in post-flight debriefs and interviews, he was confident
that the landing could proceed since the computer continued to keep Eagle stable and on the correct approach path.
At worst, the alarms were distractions, so It's doubtful
Armstrong would have initiated an abort even if Mission
Control had called for one.

The computer alarms were due to the computer's
confusion about which way Eagle's rendezvous radar is
pointing, which began when Armstrong placed the radar in
the SLEW position 3 minutes earlier. At this point in the
landing, however, no one knew what was causing the
alarms. The tension in Mission Control was undeniable,
but onboard Eagle, Armstrong was not as worried. The
alarms were a concern, but he was also very aware that
Eagle was still flying well and her other systems seemed to
be working well, so he had no intention of aborting the
landing at that point.

However, Armstrong was concerned enough about
the alarms that he chose not to use the computer to help
him retarget the landing site if the planned site was not
acceptable. Instead, Armstrong decided to "eyeball" the
surrounding area and choose a landing site purely based on
his own assessment of the situation. It was yet another
case of Armstrong employing his considerable piloting
skills and experience over the cold logic of Eagle's
computer.

~~~~

Despite the alarm, Armstrong also says to Aldrin "Let's incorporate the landing radar data." This is a critical step, as it tells the computer to take in the data from the landing radar and use it in its calculations of Eagle's altitude and velocity, essential information for a successful landing. Clearly, despite the alarm, Armstrong intends to land Eagle. As he would later say— "We had gone that far and we wanted to land ... we were focusing our attention on doing what was required in order to complete the landing."

~~~~

By the standards of the day, Eagle's computer was impressive. It was the first computer to use integrated circuits, a technology that's employed in almost every device built today. Its memory capacity was minuscule by today's standards (much, much less than that of a typical smartphone), but through clever design and programming the computer was able to control every aspect of a Moon-landing mission, from launch to landing. The computer was designed and programmed by a talented team of engineers, computer scientists and mathematicians at the Massachusetts Institute of Technology's Instrumentation Laboratory. Because of its limited memory, the MIT programmers designed the software to focus only on what was absolutely essential during critical operations, and simply drop any other tasks. This is what the 1202 alarm was telling the crew and the flight controllers. In effect, it was telling them "I'm too busy with the landing, and I'm

dropping everything else." Specifically, it was dropping the
task of trying to keep the rendezvous radar pointed at
Columbia.

~~~~

Forty seconds later the computer issues another 1202 alarm.
Although Mission Control has assured the crew that they won't pro-
hibit the landing, the alarms have an impact, because they distract
Armstrong from his primary task of looking for a suitable landing
site.

CHAPTER 12
Six Minutes to Landing

"AGS AND PGNS look real close," says Aldrin. Armstrong replies, "OK." Then he begins mumbling to himself, "No flags. RCS is good. DPS is good. Pressure is OK." Armstrong seems to be reassuring himself that all's well so far. There are no flags, i.e., no warning flags on the instrument panel. The reaction control system (RCS), the little rocket thrusters that let him maneuver Eagle, is good. The descent propulsion system (DPS), Eagle's big rocket engine, is performing well. And pressure is OK, although it's unclear what pressure he's referring to. Cabin pressure? Pressures in the RCS? The DPS?

Still concerned about Eagle's trajectory, Armstrong remarks to himself that they are still a "tad long." Something has caused Eagle's ground track to be further down range than it should be, and Armstrong knows this may cause problems during the final approach.

CHAPTER 13

Five Minutes to Landing

EAGLE IS 16,000 feet above the Moon. "And I have the window. I have the view out the window," Armstrong says. As the computer begins to tip Eagle over to a more upright position, the surface of the Moon starts to become visible at the bottom of the Lunar Module's windows.

"Eagle, Houston," Duke calls up. "It's Descent 2 to monitor. Over."

~~~~

Eagle had two separate fuel systems to provide fuel to Eagle's engines, and to provide information to Armstrong and Aldrin on the amount of fuel left, how fast it was being used, etc. Mission Control had been monitoring both systems, and they decided that the number 2 system was the most accurate, and should be used for the rest of the landing. Almost all of Eagle's systems were redundant, meaning there were actually two of everything required to safely fly Eagle. Notable exceptions were Eagle's rocket engines; there was only one for landing and one for taking off from the Moon. Both engines were designed to be extremely reliable, including using propellants that are hypergolic, meaning that the fuel and oxidizer ignited upon contact, without requiring any kind of ignition source. The engines were about as simple as possible for a rocket engine, and simplicity translates to reliability.

CHAPTER 14

Four Minutes to Landing

EAGLE IS AT "*High Gate,*" *about 7000 feet high and descending at 125 feet-per-second. Just under three miles to the planned landing site. At this point, the braking phase of the landing is over, and Eagle's computer automatically transitions to P64, the computer program for the Approach Phase of the landing. The computer begins to rotate Eagle to a more upright position, and as it does, the lunar surface slowly becomes visible to the crew. From this point on, Armstrong's job is looking out the window, either confirming that the computer is guiding them to a good landing site or, if it's not, searching for one himself.*

Armstrong says to Aldrin, "Okay. 5000, 100-feet-per second is good. Going to check my attitude control—attitude control is good." Eagle is 5000 feet above the Moon, descending at a rate of 100 feet-per-second. In preparation for the upcoming landing phase of the descent, Armstrong checks the attitude control system he will use to manually fly Eagle down to a safe, soft landing. He does this by briefly moving his pistol grip shaped control stick and observing

Eagle's response. Satisfied that it's responding the way he expects, Armstrong reports to Houston: "Manual control is satisfactory." At this point, Armstrong is a little behind schedule in performing the manual control check. Perhaps the flurry of computer alarms distracted him. At any rate, with this check complete, Armstrong is now ready to take over and fly Eagle manually.

CapCom Charlie Duke reassures Eagle's crew that they are still "GO for landing." Armstrong doesn't respond but says to Aldrin, "OK. 3000 at 70." Eagle is at 3000 feet, descending at 70 feet-per-second. Aldrin then responds to Duke: "Roger. Understand. Go for landing." He then turns to Armstrong and says "3000 feet."

Almost simultaneously another computer alarm occurs. "Program alarm ... 1201," Aldrin reports. It's been four minutes since the first program alarm.

"1201," Armstrong acknowledges. Then, perhaps to underscore that Eagle is rapidly approaching the lunar surface he adds, "OK. 2000 at 50." Eagle is at 2000 feet and descending at 50 feet-per-second. "Same type. We're Go!" CapCom Duke reassures Eagle's crew about the latest alarm. The 1201 alarm is the same type of alarm as the previous 1202 alarm. The quick thinking flight controllers responsible for Eagle's computer have determined that the alarms are solely due to "executive overload" and the computer is still performing well.

Eagle is rapidly approaching the lunar surface, and Armstrong is increasingly concerned. Outside his window the lunar surface is looming, coming closer every second. The view outside reveals a rough, rocky terrain, not at all like the rather smooth surface portrayed in the ground simulations. Unfortunately, despite the all-out reconnaissance effort by unmanned probes, ground-based telescopes, and even Apollos 8 and 10, the technology available in the late sixties simply didn't allow a close enough look at the Moon to spot all the potential hazards. Armstrong's voice betrays his increasing concern as he curtly says to Aldrin, "Give me an LPD." He's asking Aldrin to check with the computer and tell him what angle to look at to see the planned landing site. "47 degrees," Aldrin replies. Apparently Armstrong doesn't hear his response and he asks again, "Give me an LPD." Again, Aldrin replies: "Forty-seven degrees." "Forty-seven," Armstrong acknowledges. As he sites through the grid on his window, looking at the point the computer is targeting for a landing, Armstrong comments, "That's, uh, not a bad looking area."

Meanwhile, CapCom Charlie Duke is keeping up a steady chatter with Armstrong and Aldrin, but his words are falling on deaf ears; they're too busy flying Eagle to respond or, at this point, to even listen. Finally, Chief Astronaut Deke Slayton, who doesn't have an official seat in Mission Control but is sitting on a step next to Duke's console, leans over, punches Duke in his side and tells him to "shut up and let them land." At this point, there's nothing he can do to help, except to alert Armstrong and Aldrin when they're getting close to the abort limits. Anything else is a distraction.

CHAPTER 15
Three Minutes to Landing

ANOTHER 1202 PROGRAM alarm! Then another only 15 seconds later. The last thing Armstrong and Aldrin need at this point are more distracting program alarms. Fortunately, these are the last ones. From this point on, Armstrong must devote all of his attention to finding a suitable landing spot and guiding Eagle to it. It's becoming increasingly clear that the terrain is rougher than anyone had expected, and Armstrong is going to have to manually take over and find a good spot to land.

He asks for another LPD, and this time Aldrin replies, "Thirty-three degrees," and then a few seconds later, "Thirty-five degrees." As he sites on the new LPD angle, this time Armstrong doesn't like what he sees. "Pretty rocky area," he comments to Aldrin.

~~~~

Armstrong saw that the computer was taking them to a spot very near a large crater strewn with boulders the size of automobiles. At first he was tempted to try to slow Eagle down and land short of the targeted site, because the crater and boulders would be more scientifically interesting than a smooth plain. But he decided it was simply too risky to try to stop short and land there. He remembered an old maxim from his test piloting days: "When in doubt, land long." In other words, it's usually better to extend your approach and land further down the runway than to try to stop short. Besides, by this point, the computer alarms have caused him to doubt the accuracy of the computer in choosing a landing site, so he decided to go to manual control and land Eagle with just minimal assistance from the computer.

~~~~

At an altitude of about 600 feet, Armstrong toggles a switch on his control panel that tells the computer to transition to P66, the manual control mode. Armstrong is holding a small pistol grip controller in his right hand that he uses to control Eagle's attitude—the way it's pointed. The computer is still controlling the engine's throttle. He pitches Eagle forward until it's almost horizontal with the lunar surface. This increases Eagle's forward speed so that Armstrong can fly it over the boulder field. Suddenly Eagle is flying forward at a speed of about 40 miles-per-hour! The flight controllers in Mission Control are incredulous; none of the preflight simulations had the Lunar Module zipping forward at such a speed this late in the landing phase. They're unaware of the crater or the boulder field, or that

Armstrong is hopping over them looking for a good spot to land on the other side of the crater. As pilot-in-command, Armstrong is now solely responsible for landing Eagle. Mission Control cannot help him.

~~~~

In his book "A Man on the Moon," Andrew Chaikin wrote "Gene Kranz knew then (when Armstrong took over manual control) that the partnership had all but dissolved, that the center of gravity of the decision-making process was no longer some point midway between himself and the Moon. It was Neil Armstrong." Even though Armstrong was flying Eagle manually, it was unlike flying in the conventional sense that pilots are used to. His control inputs didn't pull on cables or push on actuators; rather, they were relayed to Eagle's computer, which then sent the appropriate electrical signal to either Eagle's movable engine nozzle or to the 16 thrusters positioned, in groups of four, on each corner of Eagle's blocky, irregularly shaped ascent stage. It was a type of control system known as "fly-by-wire," and in 1969 there were only two operational flying machines that used it—the Lunar Module and the Concorde supersonic transport.

While skimming over the crater, Armstrong noticed that their descent rate was still too high, and they would soon be too low to see far enough ahead to pick out a good landing spot. So he switched to a semiautomatic mode that let him control Eagle's descent rate even though the computer was actually controlling the throttle. Using a toggle switch, Armstrong could vary Eagle's descent rate in one foot-per-second increments. Thanks to his training in the LLTV, Armstrong is used to this mode of flying. It was the space age version of "flying by the seat of your pants."

CHAPTER 16
Two Minutes to Landing

EAGLE IS NOW about 300 feet above the Moon and descending at a little over three feet-per-second. Armstrong is manually flying Eagle and searching for a good spot to land. He identifies a couple of good spots, but then as he gets closer realizes they're not good after all. "I was being absolutely adamant about my right to be wishy-washy about where I was going to land," Armstrong would say later.

Although he's having difficulty finding a good landing spot, Armstrong is pleasantly surprised by Eagle's flying characteristics; it's a lot easier than he expected. It's much easier than flying the Lunar Landing Training Vehicle.

~~~~

According to the pre-mission timeline, Eagle should have landed by now. Gene Kranz wrote: "In every training run, we would have put it down by now. It is going to be close, damn close, closer than we ever trained for." But Armstrong was still looking for a place to land.

~~~~

Throughout the entire descent, Aldrin has not shown the slightest concern or alarm despite the myriad communications and computer problems he and Armstrong had encountered. Now, for the first time, he seems concerned. "Okay, you're uh, pegged on, uh, horizontal velocity," he says to Armstrong. Eagle is moving forward so rapidly that the indicator needle is "pegged," i.e., it can't register any higher. Armstrong slowly tilts Eagle backward, beginning to slow down as he clears the crater and boulders. "Slow it up. Ease her down," Aldrin advises him.

"Okay, how's the fuel?" Armstrong asks. "Eight percent," says Aldrin. "Okay, here's a … looks like a good area here," comments Armstrong. "I got the shadow out there, 250 feet, down at two-and-a-half, nineteen forward," says Aldrin.

Perhaps due to Eagle's low altitude maneuvering, the landing radar now begins to drop out. This triggers "Altitude" and "Velocity" lights on Eagle's control panel, indicating that the radar can no longer provide this data to the crew. Aldrin reports this to Armstrong, but at this point it's inconsequential. They're close enough to landing to get by without it.

Armstrong finally finds a good spot to land. "Right over that crater," he says. "I've got a good spot." His voice remains calm, but his heart rate soars to 150 beats-per-minute. "You're looking good," Aldrin reassures him.

CHAPTER 17

One Minute to Landing

"ONE HUNDRED FEET, three-and-a-half down, nine forward. Five percent. Quantity light," Aldrin reports. Eagle is 100 feet above the Moon, descending at a rate of three-and-one-half feet-per-second, and moving forward at nine feet-per-second. A red light on the instrument panel, the quantity light, illuminates, indicating that Eagle has only about five percent of its fuel remaining.

~~~~

Fuel sensors in spacecraft are notoriously unreliable since the fuel is often either in a weightless condition and/or sloshing around due to the motion of the spacecraft. Because of this uncertainty, Mission Control planned to make a "Bingo" call 94 seconds after the quantity light came on. At Bingo, Armstrong would have to make a decision: Either land within 20 seconds or abort immediately. It would be a judgment call on his part, and no instrument or flight controller or even Aldrin could advise him on it. If he didn't think he could land within 20 seconds of the Bingo call, he must abort immediately. At least that was what the Mission Rules said. It's a decision that only Armstrong, as the pilot-in-command, could make.

~~~~

"Okay, 75 feet and it's looking good," Aldrin calls out. Ever the encourager, his calm tone and optimistic words reassure Armstrong that Eagle and the approach path are both good, freeing Armstrong to concentrate on the business of manually landing Eagle. "Forward, forward, looks good," Aldrin says.

Eagle is now sixty seconds away from the Bingo time. "Sixty seconds," Duke calls up to Eagle. In sixty seconds Armstrong will have to decide if he's going to land or abort. It's likely that at this point, short of a catastrophic systems failure, Armstrong would have continued the landing regardless of the Bingo time. An abort at this point in the landing phase would be risky in the extreme. Far better to continue to a landing if at all possible, even if it meant running out of fuel while Eagle was still above the Lunar surface.

Armstrong has found his spot, and he's slowly taking Eagle down for a landing. "Forty feet, down two-and-a-half," Aldrin calls out. Then he makes a call that brings home the enormity of this occasion and makes it tangible for all those listening, "Picking up some dust."

~~~~

As the exhaust plume of Eagle's engine began disturbing the lunar dust, Armstrong encountered another problem. The dust obscured the surface; he could no longer see rocks or other surface features that allowed him to visually determine his height and speed over the surface. It was very much like trying to land an airplane with surface fog covering the runway. But fortunately Armstrong was able to see a few rocks poking up through the dust, and he used these as reference points to judge his speed across the surface. Still, it was very difficult to get a handle on how fast Eagle was moving, and Armstrong struggled to determine which way he was heading and how fast he was moving over the surface.

~~~~

"Thirty feet, two-and-a-half down, faint shadow," Aldrin reports. "Four forward, four forward, drifting to the right a little. Twenty feet, down a half."

"Thirty seconds." Charlie Duke reminds Armstrong and Aldrin that they have 30 seconds to land, or initiate an abort. Armstrong is worried about their fuel, but he has yet another "engineering ace" up his sleeve he hasn't revealed to anyone else. He knows that if he had Eagle stabilized on final approach, he could run out of fuel while above the lunar surface and still be able to make a safe and successful unpowered landing in the low lunar gravity. He knew because he had done the calculations himself, and his calculations told him that Eagle could survive a fall from at least 40 feet, possibly higher.

~~~~

By the time Eagle got below 30 feet altitude Armstrong had selected his landing site. He was also using a technique that he, no doubt, learned in his early student pilot days at Port Koneta, to ensure that he made a nice, gentle landing. He focused his eyes a little beyond the landing site. This helped him to visually judge his height and speed much more accurately. He struggled to arrest a persistent leftward movement, and he even sensed Eagle moving backwards a little. This was definitely not good, because Eagle could be backing into an unseen rock or crater, which could have been disastrous. Finally, he stopped the backward drift, making control inputs he later described as "spasmodic." But the leftward drift continued, and Armstrong was not able to stop it.

~~~~

"Drifting forward just a little bit. That's good," says Aldrin. At this point, Armstrong has passed the point of no return. For better or worse, fuel or no fuel, He's going to land Eagle on the Moon.

CHAPTER 18

Touchdown

"CONTACT LIGHT," ALDRIN reports. *At least one of the three landing probes has touched the Moon. For all practical purposes, the long, arduous journey from the Earth to the surface of the Moon is over. All that remains is for Armstrong to shut down the descent engine and allow Eagle to fall, gently and silently, onto the Moon.*

~~~~

Armstrong had planned to shut down the engine as soon as the contact light illuminated, but for some reason he didn't. Instead, he let the engine continue to run, and when he sensed that Eagle's descent had stopped, he pushed the stop button.

~~~~

Three seconds after Aldrin announces contact, Armstrong replies "Shutdown." He notices that the lunar dust cloud isn't lingering as it would on Earth, but disappears as soon as the engine stops, leaving a "perfectly clear view." Eagle settles gently down, so gently that it's hard to tell that they've landed. It will be the gentlest of all six Moon landings.

A litany of checklist items begins. Aldrin and Armstrong must complete it to ensure that Eagle is in safe condition. "ACA out of detent," Aldrin calls. Armstrong briefly moves the pistol grip controller, technically known as the Attitude Control Assembly, or ACA, and then lets the spring-loaded control stick go back to its neutral position. This tells Eagle's computer that the Lunar Module is sitting still and no longer flying. "Out of detent, Auto," Armstrong replies.

"Mode Control both Auto. Descent engine command override—off. Engine arm—off. Four-thirteen is in." Aldrin announces as he continues working through the post-landing checklist. Last on the list, Aldrin enters "10000" into the computer memory location 413. This tells the computer that Eagle is on the Moon.

"We copy you down, Eagle," Charlie Duke radios from Mission Control.

"Engine arm off," Armstrong says to Aldrin. The two turn toward each other, smile, and shake hands. Then, Armstrong switches his communications mode so that he's transmitting to Houston and announces to the world that Eagle has safely arrived on the Moon.

"Houston ... uh, Tranquility Base here. The Eagle has landed."

EPILOGUE

A FEW HOURS after touchdown, Armstrong descended down the ladder on Eagle's front leg and stepped onto the Moon. "That's one small step for man, one giant leap for mankind," he said. History records these as the first words spoken upon the Moon. Armstrong's first step onto the Moon is generally regarded as the pinnacle of the Apollo 11 mission, and indeed, of the entire Apollo Program. But Armstrong viewed it differently. On the tenth anniversary of Eagle's landing, he was asked about the importance of his famous first words on the Moon. "That wasn't the important thing I said that day," Armstrong replied. "The most important thing I said was 'The Eagle has landed.'" In another interview he said, "The exciting part for me, as a pilot, was the landing on the Moon. That was the time that we had achieved the national goal of putting Americans on the Moon. The landing approach was, by far, the most difficult and challenging part of the flight. Walking on the lunar surface was very interesting, but it was something we looked on as reasonably safe and predictable. So the feeling of elation accompanied the landing rather than the walking."

In interviews after the Apollo 11 mission, Armstrong often gave hints that, barring any other systems failures, he would have continued down to a landing regardless of what the mission rules said. In an interview with the famous World War II historian, Steven Ambrose, Armstrong commented on this. He confessed that he was concerned about running out of fuel, but he knew he could land Eagle safely even if he ran out of fuel before touchdown. "So I was perhaps probably less concerned about it than a lot of people watching down here on Earth." Armstrong told Ambrose. "That's not to say I wasn't thinking about it though, because I certainly was, but I thought it was important to try to get it down smoothly on the first try." As for the computer problems, he told Ambrose: "The vehicle was flying well, it was going down the trajectory we expected, no abnormalities in anything we saw, other than the computer saying, 'there's a problem, and it's not my fault.' The people here on the ground were right on top of that, and of course, the computer continued in a contrary manner periodically all the way to the surface. But my own feeling was, as long as everything was going well and looked right, the engine was operating right, I had control and we weren't getting into any unusual attitudes or things that looked like they were out of place, I would be in favor of continuing, no matter what the computer was complaining about." Flight Director Gene Kranz seemed to sense this as well. In his autobiography "Failure Is Not an

Option" he wrote that, in the last few minutes of the landing, "I get the feeling they are going to go for broke. I have had this feeling since they took over manual control. They are the rights ones for the job."

Armstrong initiated manual control at an altitude of about 600 feet, and he manually flew Eagle for two minutes and 18 seconds. None of the other five commanders that subsequently landed on the Moon initiated manual control at such a high altitude (the average for the remaining five Moon landings was about 330 feet), so Armstrong holds the record for the most time logged manually flying a Lunar Module. It's likely that future lunar landers will be entirely automatic, so Armstrong's record will probably never be broken.

Armstrong's flying skills were legendary, but his engineering talents also played an important role in Eagle's successful landing, and in the years following the landing he seemed to grow increasingly proud of his role as an engineer. In a speech at the National Press Club in 2002, he remarked that "I am, and ever will be, a white socks, pocket protector, nerdy engineer; born under the second law of thermodynamics, steeped in steam tables, in love with free-body diagrams, transformed by LaPlace and propelled by compressible flow." The unique techniques he helped develop to both enable and monitor Eagle's landing certainly prove that he was as talented an engineer as he was a pilot. It was a rare combination, and one that validated NASA's choice of Armstrong as the commander of the first Moon landing.

Aviation and airplanes were Armstrong's great passions. He always believed that the techniques and skills borrowed from the world of aviation had played a critical role in the manned space program. A year after Landing on the Moon he would leave NASA and return to his aviation roots as a professor of aeronautical engineering at the University of Cincinnati. He died in 2012. Collins also left NASA within a year, and went on to be the first Director of the National Air and Space Museum; he also wrote a wonderful autobiography "Carrying the Fire." Aldrin departed NASA in 1971 to return to the Air Force and become the Commandant of the Aerospace Research Pilot School at Edwards Air Force Base. Together, they had helped usher mankind into an era of exploration that is still unfolding. Future Moon landers will probably be guided to a landing by a computer. The astronauts onboard will be responsible for monitoring the systems, but they almost certainly won't be flying the landers as the astronauts of Apollo did. History will always remember that for a short time near the end of the last century, skilled pilots flew Lunar Modules down to the Moon. And Neil Armstrong and Buzz Aldrin led the way when they landed Eagle at Tranquility Base.

BIBLIOGRAPHY

NASA. **Apollo 11 Mission Audio** (https://www.nasa.gov/mission_pages/apollo/40th/apoll o11_audio.html#.XEn58NFMGf0)

Armstrong, Neil. **Wingless on Luna (Speech presented to The Wings Club)**. Copyright: Neil A. Armstrong, 1988.

Chaikin, Andrew. **A Man on the Moon**. New York: Penguin Books, 1994.

Hansen, James R. **First Man The Life of Neil A. Armstrong.** New York: Simon and Schuster, 2005.

Kranz, Gene. **Failure Is Not An Option.** New York: Simon and Schuster, 2000.

Neil Armstrong, Mike Collins, Edwin E. Aldrin, Jr. **First on the Moon**. Boston: Little, Brown and Company, 1970.

Mindel, David. **Digital Apollo**. Cambridge, MA: The MIT Press, 2008.

Kelly, Thomas. **Moon Lander**. Washington, DC: Smithsonian Institution Press, 2001.

Duke, Charlie. **Moonwalker**. Nashville, TN: Oliver Nelson Press, 1990.

NASA. **Apollo 11 Mission Report.** NASA Scientific and Technical Information Office: Washington, DC, 1971.

Matranga, Gene. **Unconventional, Contrary and Ugly— The Lunar Landing Research Vehicle**. NASA: Washington, DC, 2006.

NASA Johnson Space Center. **Oral History Project, Oral History Transcript—Neil Armstrong interviewed by Dr. Stephen E. Ambrose and Dr. Douglas Brinkley. Houston, TX. September 19, 2001.** (https://www.hq.nasa.gov/alsj/a11/ArmstrongNA_9-19-01.pdf)

NASA. **Apollo 11 Lunar Surface Journal** (https://www.hq.nasa.gov/alsj/**).**

ABOUT THE AUTHOR

Michael Engle recently retired from NASA after a 38-year career as an astronautical engineer. During that time, he worked as a design engineer (in that period he designed a new lunar landing spacecraft for future Moon missions), an astronaut training engineer, a flight controller in Mission Control, and as the Chief Engineer for Safety in the Astronaut Office. He also taught spaceflight history classes for new astronaut candidates.

Engle holds a BS in mechanical/aerospace engineering, an MS in planetary science, and an MS in aeronautical science. He also holds a commercial pilot license for both airplanes and seaplanes. He has published articles in *Astronomy Magazine*, *National Defense Magazine*, *Spaceflight Magazine* and *Air Facts Journal*.

Made in the USA
Monee, IL
01 April 2020